Contents

If any regard is to be had to the

general beauty of the landscape, the

natural material of the special

countryside should be used instead of

imported material.

William Morris, 1890

Cirencester, or Corinium as it was known then, was the second most populous settlement in Roman Britain. From the 1st to the 4th centuries, Cirencester was not a military town like Chester or York, being a civilian community, the focus of a number of important outlying villas (of which Chedworth, to the north, is the outstanding survivor), which formed the centres of farmsteads.

Roman Cirencester had a grid of streets and was protected by an enclosing wall, although both are now almost obliterated. Many of the present streets, dating from mediaeval times, are engagingly curved. Outside the line of the Roman walls, to the east of Cirencester Hospital, is a grassed-over Roman amphitheatre, which was originally constructed with limestone seating. The focus of the town is the market place. This dates from Saxon times, when it was cluttered by narrow streets (e.g. Butcher Row, Butter Row, Shoe Lane, The Shambles), which were swept away in 1830 to create the present open space; it is still used for regular markets.

The town has experienced a largely uneventful history, punctuated only by minor skirmishes of the Civil War in the 17th century. It survives today with a remarkable preservation of a number of houses dating from the 15th century, and entire streets of old buildings remain little altered since their construction. Cirencester was enthusiastically and admirably described in terms of its development and architecture in Alec Clifton-Taylor's 'Six More English Towns'.

Though the building materials of Cirencester display less variety of types compared with, for instance, Gloucester, there is much interest in understanding the materials used at Cirencester, and the story of their use in the different architectural styles employed. It is also instructive to relate these changes to the history of the town, from Roman times onward, located as it is at the hub of the Cotswolds Area of Outstanding Natural Beauty.

In mediaeval times, the Cotswolds prospered on the profits from wool from the sheep (the 'Cotswold Lions'). The area's natural woodland was cut down, and the entire Cotswolds became an expanse of bare upland fields. The limestone bedrock was responsible for the growth of rich grasses, as pasture suitable for grazing sheep. According to Shakespeare, writing about the early 14th century at the end of the 16th, when Falstaff goes recruiting here (near Stow-on-the-Wold), it was a cold, bare upland country.

The prosperity, testified to by the survival of huge churches funded by local rich woolmasters (Burford, Chipping Campden, Fairford, Northleach, Cirencester), was due to the richly calcareous Jurassic bedrock foundation, a good example of how geology underpins much that we do. Architecturally, much of the charm and beauty of the Cotswolds' buildings derive from frequent utilisation of the local limestone for cottages, houses and dry stone walling, which blends harmoniously and naturally with the local landscape.

THE GEOLOGY OF CIRENCESTER

To appreciate the building stones of Cirencester, it is necessary to understand the local rocks from which most of the building materials have been quarried.

Gloucestershire is unusual in its wide diversity of rock groups, representing most of the major geological periods, from the Cambrian to the present day (spanning a time period of over 500 million years). The distribution of these rock groups is shown in the geological map (Figure 2). The thick limestone succession that makes up the great limestone plateau of the Cotswold Hills comprises two major limestone units, the Inferior Oolite in the lower part, overlain by the Great Oolite. These rock units are of Middle Jurassic age, and represent the

Figure 2. Simplified geological map of Gloucestershire, showing distribution of major rock units. See Fig 3 for legend.

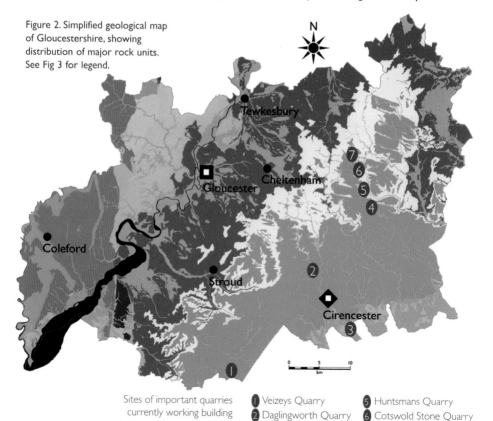

Sites of important quarries currently working building stones and aggregates in the Gloucestershire Cotswolds

1. Veizeys Quarry
2. Daglingworth Quarry
3. Cotswold Aggregates
4. Farmington Stone
5. Huntsmans Quarry
6. Cotswold Stone Quarry
7. Cotswold Hills

Bajocian and Bathonian epochs, respectively. The bedrock beneath Cirencester is the Great Oolite, the sediments of which were laid down in warm shallow seas between 167-164 million years ago (Figure 3).

The bedrock of the area was only weakly folded in the great upheaval that formed the Alps, in Cenozoic times, and the Jurassic rocks around Cirencester form part of an immense open synclinal fold with a slightly sinuous axis trending east-west through the basin to Marlborough.

The Quaternary rocks present in this area, which overlie the Middle Jurassic bedrock, form four Upper Thames Gravel Terraces. These were deposited by the flow of meltwater from the ice sheets that were situated to the north of the Cirencester area during the Pleistocene Ice Age, between 500,000 and 10,000 years ago. The southern edge of the ice sheet is known to have been located around the Moreton in Marsh area. At this time, the area around Cirencester was akin to today's Siberian tundra; home to woolly mammoths, the remains of which have been found in gravel workings in what is now the Cotswold Water Park, a few miles to the south of Cirencester.

There is thus an enormous break in the rock record in the Cirencester area, representing a time gap of more than 150 million years (equivalent to all of the Cretaceous and Cenozoic periods), between the time of the warm seas of the Jurassic and the Ice Age. Any rocks that may have been deposited in the missing interval have since been eroded, leaving the Jurassic rocks exposed, either at the surface, or beneath the Pleistocene gravels.

Time Period		Main Rock Groups	Age (millions of years)
Quaternary		Allluvium	0.01 - present
		River Terrace Gravels	0.30 - present
		Glacial Deposits	0.50 - 0.43
Jurassic	Upper	Oxford Clay & Kellaways Beds	164 - 155
	Middle	Great Oolite Group	167 - 164
		Inferior Oolite Group	175 - 167
		Whitby Mudstone	183 - 175
		Marlstone Rock	189 - 183
	Lower	Dyrham	189 - 183
		Charmouth Mudstone	196 - 189
		Blue Lias	200 - 196
Triassic		Penarth Group	203 - 200
		Mercia Mudstone Group	241 - 203
		Sherwood Sandstone	251 - 241
Permian		Bridgnorth Sandstone	299 - 270
Carboniferous		Upper Coal Measures	310 - 306
		Carboniferous Limestone	360 - 334
Devonian		Old Red Sandstone	418 - 360
Silurian		Ludlow	422 - 418
		Wenlock	428 - 422
		Llandovery	443 - 428
Ordovician		Igneous Intrusions	
		Breadstone Shales	488 - 443
		Bronsil Shale	
Cambrian		White Leaved Oak Shale	520 - 488

Figure 3. Geological succession in Gloucestershire, showing periods, main rock groups and ages.

The villages and towns which provide the Cotswolds around Cirencester with its special character are built of stone taken mainly from the local Inferior Oolite and Great Oolite limestones. Local limestone has been used for the construction of buildings, monuments, dry stone walling and roofing slates and, internally, for fireplaces. Much of the local stone used has been dug from local quarries, a few of which are still working (for example at Farmington [Northleach], Guiting Power and Chipping Campden), to meet the continuing demand for natural limestone, both locally and further afield (Figure 2).

In addition to the local building stone, several types of stones have been brought to Cirencester from other areas or countries, for their decorative appeal. Some have been used only as cladding (larvikite from Norway, travertine from Italy), while others have been employed for church features (Ashford Limestone from northern England, for church fonts), paving (York Stone), or cobbled areas (granite, basalt). In rare cases, whole buildings have been constructed primarily from stone originating from outside the town (Portland Stone from Dorset, see HSBC Bank, right).

Archaeological remains from Cirencester show that the Romans used primarily local Cotswold stone, supplemented with materials from other areas of Britain (such as Purbeck Marble) for building construction, as well as marbles from other countries for decorative purposes. Mosaics were constructed from a range of stone types from the broader local region, including hard Chalk (probably from Wiltshire), Pennant Sandstone and Old Red Sandstone from the Forest of Dean and Herefordshire, and Lower Jurassic Lias limestone from the Severn Vale.

In addition to the natural local stone, in recent times, there has been much use of 'reconstituted' stone ('Bradstone'), which is made from gravels quarried from open pits in the Upper Thames Gravels of what is now the Cotswold Water Park, a few miles to the south and east of Cirencester. The pebbles in these gravels are almost entirely composed of flattened, sub-rounded, fragments of Inferior Oolite and Great Oolite limestones that were eroded by river action from the local Jurassic bedrock during the last Ice Age. When reprocessed, the gravels are made into building blocks and roofing slates of limestone composition, that are significantly less expensive than original Cotswold stone.

CIRENCESTER
IN STONE
A TOWN TRAIL

D escribed below is a town walk that demonstrates the variety of building stones used in Cirencester, past and present, placed in the context of the historical development of the town. This trail commences at the Beeches car park, at the junction of Beeches Road and London Road (entrance on Beeches Road). There are toilets both here and at the Forum Car Park.

Please refer to the map on the inside front cover (Figure 1).

Floral design Roman mosaic from Corinium Museum.

Directions: From the Beeches car park, cross London Road and walk along Corinium Gate north-westwards and over a small bridge into the Abbey Grounds: the grassy mound on the right represents the only remaining section of the encircling Roman town wall preserved at Cirencester. The wall itself is visible on the northern side of the mound.

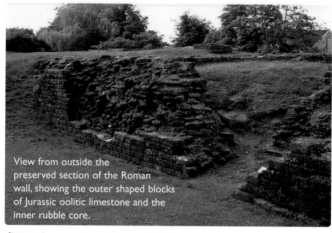

View from outside the preserved section of the Roman wall, showing the outer shaped blocks of Jurassic oolitic limestone and the inner rubble core.

The section of Roman Wall exposed here totals about two metres in thickness, and is composed of angular blocks, rather roughly shaped, forming an outer facing, one block thick, to a rubble stone core. There is another such facing on the inner (south) side of the wall.

Close up of the rubble core of shelly oolite.

The material used in the wall construction is mostly a fine shelly limestone, probably in part siliceous (photo, top left). The shell fragments are aligned in some blocks, and are up to 0.5cm in length. Some finer grained, cream-coloured oolitic limestone has also been used (see photo, bottom left).

White oolitic limestone, also used in the Roman wall.

The curved footing extension on the outer (north) side of the wall is the trace of a bastion. The preserved section includes a rectangular building, which was probably a guardroom. To the southeast, the wall continues as a grass-covered ridge passing under a modern house (see photo below) but to the northwest the ridge falls away, presumably due to removal of the stone in later years, for use elsewhere in the construction of other buildings in the town.

Continuation south-eastwards of the wall, hidden in a grassed-over ridge.

Directions: Walk north-westwards past the lake, which is a branch of the River Churn, from which the town derived its name (Churn, Ciren-, Corin- are all derivatives of the same name: the Victorian use of the pronunciation Cissester was an affectation). The lake was formerly a large fishpond from which the monks of Cirencester Abbey took fish, a staple diet of the mediaeval monasteries. Walk on to the NW corner of the Abbey Grounds and turn right onto a pathway. Immediately ahead is the Abbey Gateway.

The northern exit archway to the Abbey Grounds, a Romanesque (Norman) feature which has been widened. Note the ancient oak door.

Doorway pillar showing well-shaped masonry cornices, with rubblestone panels.

Shelly, brown, coarse-textured Jurassic limestone on the north side of the gatehouse, contrasting with the adjacent blocks of finer-grained and lighter coloured oolite.

The Abbey Gateway is the only major part of the mediaeval abbey that is standing today (there are other fragmentary remains in the Abbey grounds, which will be seen later on the trail). The gateway is somewhat incongruously joined to a modern house. The abbey was dissolved by Thomas Cromwell under Henry VIII's rule in the 16th century, as a consequence of which the structure was demolished and the stones incorporated into new town buildings.

The gateway arch appears to have been widened, and the topmost blocks are clearly replacements; which is also true of the opposite (north) side of the arch. The structure dates from the 12th century, and was originally a narrower Romanesque (Norman) round-headed arch. The wall to the right, as one approaches from the grounds, has dressings in quite good quality ashlar blocks, but the stonework to the right of this is of small irregularly-shaped rubble stones. A buff-coloured oolitic limestone has been largely used for the arch construction, but there are also occasional blocks of a distinctive dark-brown coarse shelly limestone (with curved bivalve shell fossils), that have been used here and there on the outer side of the arch (see photo, left). The same type of dark brown, shelly limestone will be seen in several other of the older buildings in the town, for example in the Woolmarket. The stones used in the arch

Cotswold slate roof of Abbey Gatehouse, showing typical arrangement of slates, increasing in size from the ridge to the eaves.

are locally quarried Jurassic (Great Oolite), rocks, which were laid down in a shallow shelf sea about 165 million years ago. The fossil shells are marine bivalves, related to the mussels seen at the coast today. Note that all the rocks display a lamination; this is bedding representing alternating deposits of fine and coarse material. On the north side of the archway, a small piece of fine–grained sandstone can be seen incorporated in the masonry. This was originally formed in the sea as a sediment, composed of fine sand and clay particles settling from sea water. It was originally soft, but has been hardened by cementation of calcite within the sediment, following deposition and subsequent burial.

Note the arch of the doorway in the house to the northwest: this ogee-headed style did not appear until Tudor times, around 1500. Observe also the ancient oak door to the archway. Look up to the

Stone slates: many buildings in the Cotswolds are roofed by 'stone slates', which are not true slates, but fissile limestones from the Jurassic sequence that split naturally into thin layers suitable for roofing. They are commonly known as 'Stonesfield Slates' from a locality near Stonesfield in Oxfordshire. They are very heavy, and are therefore always graded from small to large, from ridge to eaves.

Quarrymen devised wonderful, illogical names for the various sizes and these names vary from county to county. These rocks split into flat sheets, especially after being subject to weathering and frost, and their colour tones in well with the wall material. These local slates were much cheaper than imported true slates from Wales or Cornwall (which have been used in some buildings in Cirencester).

Cotswold slate types and roof construction (from Dreghorn, 1967).

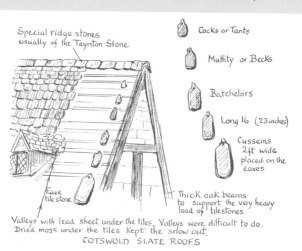

Special ridge stones usually of the Taynton Stone

Cocks or Tants

Muffity or Becks

Batchelors

Long 16 (23 inches)

Cussems 2ft wide placed on the eaves

Eave tile stone

Thick oak beams to support the very heavy load of tilestones.

Valleys with lead sheet under the tiles, Valleys were difficult to do. Dried moss under the tiles kept the snow out.

COTSWOLD SLATE ROOFS

Directions: Walk southwards across the Abbey Grounds towards the church tower.

The Abbey grounds.

Bridge in the Abbey grounds.

The modern houses seen to the right of the path are built of artificial stone — 'Bradstone'. Further along the pathway, on the left, will be seen a crescent of stone walling with seats, and a series of stones set in the green lawn. This marks the site of the now destroyed Cirencester Abbey church, a huge building which may have dated partly from Saxon times. This was situated closely alongside the present day St John the Baptist Parish Church, and its graveyard. The present church was completed in the 15th-16th century, but there was once an older church building on the site, from which some Romanesque (Norman) work is preserved within the present building.

The outlines indicated by square slabs in the grass demonstrate the enormous size of the former Abbey Church: the oldest part of the nave was originally located through the hedge to the west. The north transept is marked out with an eastern curved chapel, a

Remains of the destroyed Cirencester Abbey church.

Remains of column and trough.

curved apse behind the altar and, behind this, a wide rectangular area with more chapels. The Abbey probably had no south transept, this side being occupied by functional buildings. A few fragments of the existing Abbey remain, including the remains of a column and trough (see photos, left), both constructed from local oolitic limestone. On the western side of the Abbey grounds can be seen a well constructed dry stone wall (see photo below).

A dry stone wall in the Abbey Grounds, utilising shaped (dressed) blocks of Jurassic limestone. This method, used for town walls, contrasts with the skilful use of unshaped stone blocks in the construction of Cotswolds field walls.

Dry stone walling: the art of dry stone walling is centuries old and is practised in country districts where limestone is abundantly available, such as the Cotswolds. There are two forms of walling; the very rough variety where the stones are quite unshaped (suitable for field boundaries), and the type seen here where roughly shaped, flattened oblong blocks are utilised. This is preferred in town walls. No cement is used to bind the stones, and there is considerable skill in selection of the correct blocks, so the wall does not collapse. The most durable walls have some protection from the rain, preventing it penetrating deep into the inside; this may be in the form of a layer of stones arranged on their edges ('toppers') or a thin overlay of mortar, as in this case.

Directions: Walk to the left (north) along a path, following the dry stone wall on your right (described opposite). Cross a small bridge over a branch of the River Churn, turn right along a passage to a roadway (Waterloo Road). Opposite, the archway entrance to the Woolmarket will be seen.

The Woolmarket area comprises a walkway through a shopping area, with a mixture of buildings of both modern and period date. The buildings in the northern part of the Woolmarket area are of modern construction, in 'Bradstone', but the buildings in the southern half, adjacent to Dyer Street, are much older, dating from the mediaeval and 16th-18th century periods.

The paving in this area is interesting and includes, at the northern end, smooth blue-grey sandstone (a widely used paving stone called 'York Stone', which originates from the Carboniferous Coal Measures south of Leeds, Yorkshire). This rock type has been used commonly in paved areas in many towns and cities across the country. At the southern end of the Woolmarket paved area, a laminated sandstone, which is probably Carboniferous Pennant Sandstone from the Forest of Dean, has also been used. The whole paved area has panels framed by long, narrow blocks of quite coarse-grained (porphyritic), Cornish granite, which displays some large white feldspar crystals set within it. Both the sandstone and granite rock types are hard and durable materials, that are able to withstand the tread of countless feet over a period of many years. Limestone is softer and does not wear so well, and is therefore not so suitable for paving in public places.

The entrance to the Woolmarket on Dyer Street comprises an archway that is constructed of interesting brown and white

A view of the south side of the Woolmarket. Note the building on the left, with rough shelly limestone stonework and ashlar window surrounds; beyond it is a building faced with 'Bradstone'. The pavement is of sandstone ('York Stone'), with linear panels of Cornish granite. The sheep statue behind is cast in bronze.

limestone blocks, in which fossil shells are prominent and distinctive (see photo, left). Inside the arch, on both right and left, are walls primarily of undressed limestone, with dressings of well-shaped blocks of limestone.

Large bivalve ('cockle') fossil shell in brown limestone block near Woolmarket entrance from Dyer St.

On the corner of the archway, on its western side, there is a section of brownish shelly limestone with numerous curved Jurassic fossil bivalve shells, up to 2-3 cm across, gastropods (snails) and brachiopods. This limestone is a shallow-water marine sedimentary rock type of Jurassic age (we know this because these organisms only live in quite shallow coastal waters in the present day). The use of this distinctive brown shelly limestone rock is typical of several of the mediaeval buildings in the town (it will be recalled that this is the same type of limestone that was seen in occasional blocks in the Abbey Gateway), which suggests that, in the Woolmarket archway, this material represents a much older, probably mediaeval, period of construction than for the buildings beside it.

In contrast, the buildings to the west of the Woolmarket entrance in Dyer Street comprise a set of 18th-19th century edifices in good dressed oolitic limestone ashlar, containing much more thinly scattered shells. Note also how a dark-brown (more iron-stained) or cream-coloured ragstone has been used for the footings of these buildings. This is, in part, due to the coarser-textured ragstone

Fossils: fossils are either the remains of animals or plants, or direct evidence of their presence (e.g. footprints and burrows, known as 'trace fossils'), preserved in rocks. Fossil types include petrified shells, bony parts of animals, skeletons, imprints of animal structure in fine claystones, leaf and fern imprints and fossil wood. Also found are microscopic forms - 'microfossils' - which can include foraminifera (animals), and algae, diatoms, spores and pollen (plants). Fossils only very rarely retain the original organic material that made up the organisms, and are usually mineral replacements preserving the original outlines and shapes.

No. 5 Dyer Street is one of a row of Georgian buildings constructed from fine oolite ashlar. Note the brown ragstone used in the footings for improved strength and that the doorsteps, which receive hard wear, are constructed from a green-grey sandstone.

being much stronger than the fine oolite, ashlar freestone; also the bedding (layers of shell fragments) in the ragstone acts as a barrier to rising damp. Ragstone has frequently been used to such effect in many buildings of the town. The two buildings at the western end of Dyer St (e.g. No. 5), display doorway footings of a greenish, medium-grained sandstone, chosen for its hardness (see photo above).

Oolitic Limestone:

a sedimentary rock, commonly used as a building stone (e.g. Portland Stone, Bath Stone, Cotswold Stone, Lincolnshire Limestone). Composed mainly of calcite, with or without some magnesium carbonate, it fizzes when treated with dilute hydrochloric acid (HCl). Many limestones contain fossils, having been formed in ancient shell banks or reefs. However, some of the most sought after building stones are largely made up of small rounded bodies, called 'ooliths'. These were formed by mechanical and chemical accretion on warm sea floors, as is happening now off the Bahamas. Some of the best building stones in the country are oolitic limestones, due to the fact that they can be cut evenly in any direction ('freestone'). Many of these have been used in Cirencester.

Ashlar: the finest masonry is composed of ashlar - squared-off blocks with smoothed surfaces, fitting together very closely with a minimum of mortar between. The oolitic limestones of the Cotswolds are reasonably soft when quarried, and can be cut easily into such blocks. After erection in masonry walls and subsequent exposure to the weather, they harden and, although initially light coloured, tend to weather to rather darker hues. No. 5 Dyer Street shows excellent oolite ashlar of a very pale hue, whereas the building between the Kings Head Hotel and the HSBC Bank on the other side of the street, shows the deep orange-brown coloration typical of oolite from the North Cotswolds, beyond Chipping Norton around Great Tew. This darker colouration is due to the presence of much more iron oxide in the limestone, than in the local south Cotswolds stone from around Cirencester.

On viewing the Woolmarket entrance from the opposite side of Dyer Street, it becomes apparent that the archway from the Woolmarket to Dyer Street is in fact cut through a house much older than those to the left of the arch. The house is probably of early 17th century origin, having had leaded casements, with the square windows being added later. A similar feature will be seen later in the walk at Dunstall House.

Larvikite cladding on an estate agent's shop in Dyer Street (No. 14), opposite the Woolmarket entrance.

Cladding: due to its cost, the use of natural building stone for construction has long been in decline, although during the last twenty years it has made a comeback in the form of ornamental cladding. This is possible because improvements in cutting technology and automation of the dressing and finishing processes, allow stone to be cut in thin sheets, making the use of stone affordable and the cladding relatively lightweight.

Polished stone is used as a rule, but unpolished stone may also be utilised. The use of cladding has given rise to a requirement for testing of the properties of cladding materials: besides the need to avoid iron staining - due to iron oxide minerals present - it is essential to test thermal properties; some rocks in thin slabs buckle due to thermal change and tend to detach, potentially endangering passers by in the street.

The estate agent's premises at 14 Dyer Street, opposite the Bear Inn, displays a cladding of larvikite; a distinctive black, iridescent igneous rock from Norway.

Notice the rectangular blocks used to form a cobbled area in front of the Bear Inn (a 17th-century building with 'jetty' overhangs on the corner). These blocks are of various igneous rock types; granites (pink), diorites (greenish-grey), and basalts (black), mixed with light-coloured quartzite (a metamorphosed sandstone). Such blocks of hard rock are used throughout the country for this purpose, for non-vehicular surfaces and crossings, and come mostly from quarries in the Midlands or Channel Islands.

Larvikite: the buildings of Cirencester do not display igneous rocks except in cladding materials. Larvikite is a commonly used cladding material; a syenite from Norway displaying attractive anorthoclase feldspars, which flash on polished surfaces in rainbow colours (iridescence), on account of minute inclusions along the cleavage planes. Intrusive igneous rocks such as this display well-formed crystals of their component minerals. This stone is used widely, in many countries, both for building cladding and also, increasingly, for kitchen work tops. It is usually referred to as granite although, due to its mineral composition, it is not strictly speaking, a granite.

Other igneous rocks being used for cladding in Cirencester, are gabbro and true granite; which have similar crystalline textures, but with different mineral composition.

Cobbles in the pavement to the front of the Bear Inn.

5. Corn Hall and adjacent buildings, Market Square

Directions: Walk along the south side of Dyer Street, west, towards the Market Square.

Nat West Bank: of oolitic limestone, with larvikite footings and doorstep.

There is a group of three buildings here, on the south side of the square, each constructed from oolitic limestone. The Nat West Bank displays a late twentieth century frontage in a yellowish oolite, which may be imported Bath Stone or more local Campden Stone (it has been chosen to match the honey coloured stone of the upper storey). This facing has a footing of larvikite. Barclays Bank, next door, is of a lighter oolite, but it's similar to that used in the Nat West Bank; again, this is a modern frontage. The Corn Hall, a building dating from 1862, is fronted with a cream-coloured oolite and has high quality carvings of swags and fruit above the entrance, together with several interesting tympana carvings, all in the fine oolite stone. All these are facades, the body of the building being built, where not exposed to view, of poorer quality materials.

The Corn Hall.

Carvings on the oolitic limestone façade of the Corn Hall. The fine Jurassic limestones carve very well.

The building on the western side of the Kings Head is one of the most striking in the town, though the imposing effect has been lessened by the presence of shop frontages. Two pillars are exposed at street level, where they can be seen to be composed of a highly distinctive, dark yellowish brown limestone (akin to the ferruginous Cotswold limestones north of Chipping Norton), which is greasy weathering but bright yellow in cut surface. This building in its upper storeys is extremely handsome, with pedimented windows, a central 'Green Man' sculpture and swags higher up, all crowned by a central pediment enclosing a mini-triple Venetian window within the pediment triangle. This building is somewhat older than the Corn Hall, as it appears to be present in an 1840 drawing of the Market Place: it may be of a Regency or even 18th century date.

A fine building of Georgian or Regency style, on the south side of Dyer Street. It is fronted by ashlar blocks of a rich brown Jurassic limestone; a type that occurs naturally in Northamptonshire. The colour is due to a higher iron content. These stones weather less well than the paler limestones of the Cirencester area.

6. HSBC Bank

Directions: Walk in a westerly direction to the junction of Market Square and the north end of Cricklade Street.

The HSBC Bank building, of Portland Stone, which is both attractive and weathers well.

The white limestone of this building is uppermost Jurassic Portland Stone from the Isle of Portland, Dorset, which contrasts in colour, composition and appearance with the local Cotswold limestone. You may ask, "Why bring limestone from the coast, when the town is built on limestone?", but the reason is that Portland Stone is the premier building stone of England and many prominent public buildings in London are built of it; St Paul's Cathedral being a prime example. Note the curved shell fossils, many several centimetres across, within the stone.

As with the Cotswold Jurassic limestones, these fossils are bivalves, and there are also trace fossils where an organism laid a trail while feeding. The white colour is due to the fact that the conditions of oxidation of the iron seen in Cotswold Stone never affected the Portland Stone, though it is also an oolitic limestone. Portland Stone's other primary quality is its strength. This is due to infilling, after burial, of the micropores on the ooliths by calcite cement; the strength being in the ooliths. Similarly, in Bath Stone the strength is in calcite cement between the pores, although in Cotswold Stone the micropores in the ooliths, and the spaces between them, are not filled by cement, and these limestones are consequently less durable.

Close-up of the Portland Stone in the HSBC Bank, showing the dark outlines of quite large bivalve shells.

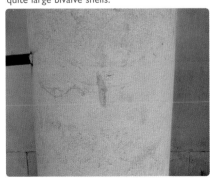

The north side of the Market Square is dominated by the St John Baptist Church, which is constructed in the 15th century perpendicular architectural style. The church tower and immense three storied porch are remarkable, the porch being the largest of any church in England. Around the tower you can see much use of a cross-bedded Jurassic ragstone, especially in wall footings and large buttresses, but inside the church finer grained oolitic limestone dominates. Notice the fine fan-vaulting of the ceilings, in the porch (see photo opposite) and St Catherine's Chapel. Fan-vaulting, which reached its supreme development in Kings College Chapel Cambridge, was a peculiarly English invention, and was apparently first used in the cloisters of Gloucester Cathedral.

View of St. John Baptist Church, showing the tower and the immense late 15th century three-storey porch.

Ragstone: this is not a geological term, but is used widely to refer to coarse-grained shelly limestone used for building purposes, for example for dry-stone walling and wall footings.

St. John Baptist Church: the tower was originally intended to be capped by a spire, but subsidence of the foundations occurred and the upper storey was added instead, hence the architectural incongruity. The buttresses, in shelly, cross-bedded ragstone for strength, were added at the same time, to prop up the tower.

Marble: long used as an ornamental stone in tombs and monuments, it is also utilised as a cladding material. True marble is a metamorphic rock, created from a limestone by heating and/or pressure, while buried. Simple burial will not produce marbles, which require either thermal- (contact with an igneous intrusion) or high-pressure (regional) metamorphism in order to form. The original sedimentary limestone rock is recrystallised to a mosaic of interlocking grains of carbonate minerals.

It is recorded that the porch structure was built in 1500, as an office for the abbot and the town hall. Why the abbey authorities would pay to have such a sumptuous building, including a fan-vaulted ceiling to the passage leading into the church, can be explained by the fact that the abbot was empowered by the king manorially and was supreme in the town at this time. If it was built to glorify the abbot, pride came before a fall, for the abbey was dismantled in 1539 by edict of Thomas Cromwell, although the rooms above the porch were later used as a town hall. The paving and steps here are of sandstone.

There is not much contrast in the building materials in the interior of the church, but the font (see photo below), mounted on a plinth of distinctive dark limestone at the west end of the nave, reveals many numerous elongated fossil crinoid stems, in Carboniferous Ashford Limestone from Derbyshire. There is another

Fine fan-vaulting of the ceiling in the porch.

St. John Baptist Church: the main font in the church has a pedestal of crinoidal limestone; here only sections through the stems are seen. However, crinoids are branching organisms attached to the sea bed, known colloquially as 'sea-lilies' (crinoids are echinoderms, related to sea urchins and star fish).

Crinoids: are members of the sea urchin order (echinoderms), characterised by their five-fold symmetry and a disc-shaped globular body enclosed by calcareous plates. From this body appendages, commonly branched, hang down; there is a stem below the body. Crinoids are common as fossils, and first appeared in Ordovician time (450 million years ago). They are still living today ('sea lilies'), although they are much rarer in the present day than in the geological past.

font in the north-eastern chapel, of true marble, white with dark veins, probably Carrara Marble from Tuscany, Italy (see photo, left). On the right hand side of this chapel there is a Jacobean tomb constructed of an assortment of marbles, with a figure in alabaster. One pillar on the right hand side of the chancel includes Roman work.

St. John Baptist Church: the second font in one of the chapels is made of a white marble (probably Carrara Marble from Italy).

St. John Baptist Church: late 15th century stonework fan-vaulting, in St. Catherine's Chapel. This requires large single masses of Cotswold limestone to be quarried; its construction is a mediaeval engineering masterpiece.

Alabaster: is a form of gypsum, a hydrated calcium sulphate, which occurs in evaporitic deposits (left behind following the evaporation of mineral rich waters), such as are common in Permian and Triassic rocks in Central England. It is very easy to carve into figures, but its use is restricted to interior monuments.

Directions: Leave the church and walk across to the west side of Gosditch Street. Here several shops have a cladding of larvikite, in this case a very dark variety.

Travertine cladding fronting shop in Gosditch St.

A t the south end of Gosditch Street is a shop (at present occupied by 'Wall Space' picture framers): this building is faced by cladding of cream-coloured travertine, a distinctive type of limestone characterised by wavy-banded algal growths. This particular variety comes from Tivoli, Italy and has been much used in Italian buildings through history. The holes that originally formed where reeds were once present have been artificially filled in this example. This type of cladding has been widely used by McDonald's restaurants, throughout the country.

> **Travertine:** is a finely crystalline limestone, with undulose banding, formed by rapid precipitation of carbonate minerals by warm or hot springs, accompanied by algal (simple plant) growth.

Close-up of travertine cladding showing the wavy, laminated texture.

Directions: Continue northwards along Gosditch Street and into Dollar Street: turn left into the narrow entry to Coxwell Street (cars not allowed).

The streets northwest of St John the Baptist church, include Dollar Street, whose name derives from the Abbey's 'dole yard' for wayfarers: at a certain time of day they received a dole of wine and bread: you can still receive this at St. Cross, Winchester. Dollar Street - and the nearby Thomas, Gloucester and Park Streets - contains a wealth of mediaeval, 17- and 18th century buildings, including a number of large former residences of wool magnates, marked by blue identification plaques. The woolmasters would have carried out their business from these buildings. Most are built of local Cotswold Jurassic oolitic limestone, with some sandstone dressings and occasional use of ragstone, particularly as footings. Many of the buildings have Cotswold stone roof slates. Coxwell Street is the best preserved of these streets and there is a booklet on sale in the town dealing solely with its history (Berkeley & Turner, 2000).

Doorway at No. 1 Coxwell Street, with a 4-centred arch, characteristic of Tudor buildings. The paving slabs are sandstone (York Stone).

Note how, on the left-hand (south) side of the street, the small houses are floored below street level; the town street level having been gradually raised up over the years. Coxwell Court, on the left-hand (south) side of the street, has two gateway pillars with inset panels of the distinctive and attractive Dagham Stone. This is a type of hard, white, sparsely oolitic Jurassic limestone that typically occurs in the area of Daglingworth (or 'Dagham') Downs, north of Cirencester. The stone is criss-crossed with numerous irregular cavities, which represent borings made by an organism, through already partly hardened rock on a hardground surface.

Gateway pillar at Coxwell Court, showing ornamental use of blocks of Dagham Stone.

Hardground: a limestone surface that has been cemented and hardened on the sea-floor shortly after deposition (rather than much later following deep burial by younger sediments, as in normal limestone formation). The hardground surface may be encrusted, discoloured, case-hardened, bored and solution-ridden. A hardground represents a gap in deposition and may mark a disconformity.

Borings contrast with burrows, made originally by burrowing organisms, such as crabs, in soft sediment, prior to lithification, or rock formation. The cavities in the Dagham Stone have been enlarged by dissolution from underground and surface waters. Dagham Stone has been often used in the Cirencester and Tetbury areas as a rockery stone. It has been used to great effect in the Cirencester Park Gateway (see below).

10. St John's Hospital

Directions: return to Dollar Street and walk northwards to the next right hand turn, Spitalgate Lane.

On the north-west side of Spitalgate Lane is the early gothic ('Early English') St John's Hospital, with its typical and attractive, simple pointed arches. This is a remnant of St John the Evangelist's Hospital, formerly a rest home for the destitute, founded in 1133 by Henry I and dissolved by Henry VIII in 1539. The building stone is composed of rough, undressed oolite masonry, with dressed oolite in the arches.

St. John's Hospital, a gothic (early English) building founded by Henry I in 1133. The gothic arch had recently replaced the rounded Romanesque arch at this time.

Directions: Return a few yards to Dollar Street, and turn right into Gloucester Street, which has been converted to a quiet backwater by traffic diversion, but which was once a main thoroughfare and scene of urban activity.

Powell's School (1740), on the left hand side, displays a side wall with exaggerated rustication in the form of stepped out alternate ashlar blocks of oolite in the dressings ('Gibbs surrounds') (see photo, right).

Further down the street, on the same side, No 33 Gloucester Street (see photo below) has a jetty overhang, a device to allow material to be passed easily in former times to and from the street level to the upper storey. It is a 15th century building, but has utilised some 'robbed' stone blocks for its footings, either from the Abbey after it was dissolved or as a later alteration, as the Abbey was not dissolved until 1540.

Powell's School, dating from 1740, showing exaggerated rustication in the form of 'Gibbs surrounds'.

No. 33 Gloucester Street, a 15th century building with a jetty. Some stone from the Abbey was later 'robbed' to provide the low footing wall; this is a distinctive brown shelly oolite of a type also seen in the Abbey Gatehouse.

91 Gloucester Street.

Nos. 91-93 Gloucester Street. Such 17th century buildings in Gloucester Street utilise large, shaped limestone slabs for the window and door surrounds, but smaller, poorly-shaped slabs for the panels between, where lime wash originally covered the wall (traces of which can still be seen).

Further along, the construction of No's. 91-93 illustrates a common practice - freestone coigns (projecting corners) and window dressings of shelly oolite freestone - frame rubblestone panels, on the surfaces of which traces of the original lime wash can be seen. Footings are mostly of ragstone.

Note the 17th century 'Drowners' Cottages on the right hand side, at the north end of the street: the drowners supervised the water meadows which formerly flanked the banks of the River Churn which runs a short distance to the north of these cottages, and which periodically still floods the area.

The Drowners' Cottages (17th century): these are of poorer construction, with no stone surrounds to the windows and the walls entirely of whitewashed, poorly-shaped masonry.

12. Thomas Street

Directions: Retrace your steps. Re-enter the north end of Dollar Street, take the first turning on the right into Thomas Street. Note on the corner that No.53 Dollar Street has primitive rustication; the freestone has been ornamented with pick marks from a mason's sharp pointed tool.

Right & below: St. Thomas's Hospital (Weavers Hall). A mixture of cream and brown limestone blocks is used randomly, the footing is of brown shelly limestone, some blocks of which show cross-bedding.

S t. Thomas's Hospital, the first building on the right (north) side of the street, has small windows and a heavy limestone block construction. Founded by Sir William Nottingham as an almshouse in 1483, it is the oldest non-ecclesiastical building in the town. A short distance further along the street, on the north side, is a building currently occupied by Tanners Solicitors. This house displays a footing (see photo at bottom of page) of the

Rustication: there are two principal types of this architectural device, aiming to give a rough appearance resembling natural rock faces to masonry in ashlar blocks. The alternate blocks in dressings such as window-frames may be stepped out or the sides of blocks may be bevelled: the second form is artificial roughening of the block face using punches. The stepping-out style is known as 'Gibbs surrounds', as it was much used in the 18th century by the architect of St. Martins in the Field, London, James Gibbs.

Tanners solicitors' building: coarse brown shelly limestone footing, showing weathering out of shells, mainly bivalves. Linear echinoid spines are visible (upper right). This is a much later building than others which have also included this rock (e.g. Weavers Hall, Wool Market), and shows that this type of stone was available over a long period of time, although this later use may have been sourced from the Abbey ruins.

The Mead House (17th century): constructed of fine oolite ashlar blocks with ornamental 'Gibbs surrounds' on the windows and doorway.

The doorstep of the Mead House: of hard wearing shelly sandstone: displaying linear ripple marks formed in soft shelly sand in a shallow sea more than 150 million years ago. Note lens cap for scale.

distinctive brown shelly limestone type already noted at the Woolmarket, the Abbey Gateway and 33 Gloucester St., suggestive of an origin from the Abbey. Walk around the corner of the building and look in the footings for the prominently displayed fossils. Besides the curved outline of bivalve shells, you will see linear echinoid spines. These protrude from the rock due to the weathering out of the matrix around them by wind and rain.

On the left (south side) of the street is the Quaker Meeting House, dating from 1677. The Quakers were anathema to the intolerant Cromwellian puritans (as were Anabaptists and the Ranters: the latter partook of unseemly orgies in public houses and preached that there was no such thing as sin!). This must have been one of the earliest Quaker foundations after the Restoration, when this very strict sect became legal.

Further along on the right hand (north) side is Mead House. This fine 18th century property, formerly owned by William Cripps, a town banker, has rusticated dressings, achieved by stepping out alternate blocks of ashlar freestone oolite. The doorway paving is an excellent example of a ripple-marked shelly sandstone. These marks were made by wave ripples in shallow water before the sand was buried and hardened.

Notice Tontine House on the right (a tontine is a particular type of will or testament: an early Bathurst profited from one). Observe, too, on the opposite side of Thomas St. from Mead House, the entrance to the Woolgatherers Warehouse and Dunstall House (a misnomer for "Gumstool House" after the brook of that name), which is a Jacobean house converted to Georgian with square windows but "all the wrong proportions", (Clifton-Taylor, 1984).

The 17th century warehouse of "Woolgatherers" nearby, the seat of another of the Cripps woolmasters. The brown shelly limestone has been skillfully used in the footings and sills between the floors to effect contrast.

Ornamental Gateway

Directions: Continue past Cicely Hill, leading to Cirencester Park, and turn left into Park Street.

This gateway is constructed of ashlar freestone oolite framing striking panels of Dagham Stone, other examples of which were previously seen in Coxwell Court, Coxwell Street. The Dagham Stone infill in the park gateway has been used to great ornamental effect in this impressive arch, which constitutes a well known and distinctive town landmark. Observe the distinctive holes in the stone, which represent borings by long-extinct Jurassic marine organisms. Notice also the immense yew hedge, allegedly the tallest in the country, here shielding the Bathurst mansion from view.

Close up of Dagham Stone infilling panels.

Ornamental gateway to Cirencester Park, the mansion of Earl Bathurst, whose ancestors originally came over with William the Conqueror. Dagham Stone has been utilised here in the cobbly panels beside the rusticated archway.

Sedimentary and 'Way Up' Structures: Geologists frequently wish to know whether the rocks exposed in an outcrop are overturned by folding or not. Surprisingly, it took a century, for the indicators of 'way-up' (mainly sedimentary structures and pillow lavas) to be eventually recognised in the first half of the 20th century. Cross-bedding is very common in sedimentary rocks and occurs in both water-laid and wind-deposited clastic sediments (those composed of rock and mineral particles). It is quite easy to detect the asymptotic bottoms and truncated tops where cross-bedding is developed. Graded-bedding, produced as the large particles sink before the finer particles, is also quite common and easily utilised. There are also small-scale unconformities, including scours, evident where deposition has given way to erosion of the top deposits or deformation by soft sediment slumping has disturbed the underlying beds before new beds were laid down above.

14. Silver Street, Park Street & Tetbury Road pavements

Silver St. Paving slab of Carboniferous 'York Stone'. This slab shows sedimentary structure, formed in flowing water, in the form of graded bedding.

Diagenesis: the primary sedimentary structures referred to above, which were formed as the sediment was laid down, can be distinguished from structures superimposed after burial due to chemical and mineral changes (diagenesis). In the Silver Street paving slabs there are many brown bands transecting the sedimentary structures and these represent iron staining. These are known as 'Liesegang's Rings', produced by chemically charged waters circulating in the rock after burial: while the main deposit is iron, manganese may also be redeposited in this way.

The stone pavements of in Silver Street are slabs of a variety of coarse-grained sandstone (a modern type of York Stone, from the Upper Carboniferous of the Pennines area) and display a wealth of sedimentary structures. These structures were probably formed in an ancient river delta. The two types of sedimentary structures that are most evident in these slabs are cross-bedding and graded bedding. Superimposed on the structures are brown ferruginous bands, which represent staining by groundwater circulating through the pore spaces between the sand grains in this rock: a diagenetic process occurring after burial. In one or two slabs angular unconformities are visible. Similar pavements have been used also in Park Street and Tetbury Road.

Paving slab showing cross-bedding, also formed in flowing water: curved foresets, as seen here, indicate a river or delta channel setting.

Directions:
Cross Silver Street and enter
Corinium Museum.

Just beyond Dunstall House in Park Street is the Corinium Museum, at the west end of Silver Street. The museum contains an exceptional collection of Roman artefacts, including remains of buildings which attest to the former grandeur of the town in Roman times. The collections include many mosaics, ornate column capitals and mouldings, illustrating the use of a range of stones in building construction and decoration, both internal and external.

Mosaics: the Romans frequently used mosaics as flooring materials in their villas. Those in the Cirencester Museum have a limited range of colours, but do include red. In some mosaics, such as those at Ostia, the ancient port of Rome, only black and a light shade were used, possibly due to the lack of suitably coloured stones in the vicinity. The mosaicist shaped the small squares of natural stone ('tesserae') of different colours and harmonised them in intricate designs. White and pale brown limestone, Blue Lias limestone, dark brown granite, red sandstone or brick were commonly used in the Cirencester mosaics.

On entering the museum, two high quality mosaics can be seen in the entrance foyer, one depicting a dolphin and the other a floral design (both illustrated here). Close examination of the component pieces (tesserae) of these mosaics shows that a range of stone types have been used in their construction, the colours of these different types being used to great artistic effect. The three primary colours of these and other mosaics are red, white and blue, complimented by the subtle juxtaposition of pastel shades afforded by the use of a diversity of stone types, usually of local origin. The main stones used in these and other Roman mosaics, and their corresponding colours, are; white (hard Chalk, oolitic Cotswold

Roman dolphin mosaic from Cirencester, in Corinium Museum, composed of tesserae of various local natural rocks.

limestone, Carboniferous Limestone), reds, orange (chopped brick and tile, Samian vessels, Old Red Sandstone, Purbeck Marble), grey/blues (Jurassic Lias limestone, Purbeck Marble, shale), purples, greys, browns, green (Pennant Sandstone). Occasionally, imported marble was used, possibly from masons' off-cuts.

Close up of Roman floral design mosaics from Cirencester. Visible stone types include hard Chalk, brown Old Red Sandstone, grey Lias limestone.

A display case on the ground floor contains several examples of stone types that have been used in the external and internal decoration of Roman buildings in Cirencester. Exhibit 7 is a piece of Purbeck Marble moulding, brought from Dorset. Exhibit 8 comprises a selection of fragments of marble wall veneers, imported from abroad (see photo on next page).

Roman Purbeck Marble decorative building mouldings, Corinium Museum.

Imported exotic marbles, used for internal wall decoration on a Roman building from Cirencester in Corinium Museum.

Elsewhere on the ground floor, two impressive column capitals can be seen, constructed from local Cotswold oolitic limestone. The Corinthian Capital is the largest ever found from Roman Britain, originating from the site of the Corinium Basilica. The Jupiter Capital (shown here) is heavily decorated with volutes and acanthus leaves typical of the Corinthian order. On each of the four sides a half-figure is carved, which have been identified with Bacchus, Silenus (male figure with drinking horn, see photo) and King Lycurgus. The fourth is an unidentified female figure. Sacred columns like this one were often dedicated to Jupiter (king of the gods). About 150 Jupiter columns are known, mainly from the Rhineland, although their capitals are usually smaller than this one.

The Roman Jupiter column capital, of local oolitic limestone, formerly located in the forum. The figure is of Silenus.

16. St James Place Headquarters Building

Directions; On exiting the museum, turn right into Black Jack Street, and then first left into Park Street. Turn right into Old Tetbury Road and second left into Hammond Way, opposite Waitrose. St James Place is on the right hand side and can be approached via a short walkway.

The St James Place building was constructed in 2007, and is strikingly clad with an attractive limestone. At first sight this appears to be Cotswold stone, but is in fact Clipsham Stone, a variety of Lincolnshire Limestone, which originated from Medwell Quarry in Rutland. The reason Lincolnshire Limestone, rather than local Cotswold Limestone was used is because the large quantity of cladding stone required for this building was not available from working local quarries. Cladding requires thin, lightweight sheets (see Miglio, 1996). Medwell Quarry has been equipped since 2002 with very modern bridge chain-saw equipment, which enables the Clipsham Stone to be supplied with a remarkable degree of uniformity of colour, composition and thickness. The St James Place building, which utilises cladding 17mm thick, displays this to a marked degree.

Exterior view of the building showing the aesthetically effective and generous use of attractive Clipsham Stone limestone cladding with prominent cross bedding.

A narrow belt of Lincolnshire Limestone, continuous with, and of the same age as the Inferior Oolite of the Cotswolds, conveniently runs north-south through Lincoln city where it was used in the construction of the Cathedral and Lincoln's many famous churches. The Romans used Lincolnshire Limestone both in Lincoln and in London, the famous London Stone originally in Cannon Street, believed to be the stone from which the Romans measured their road distances, is reportedly of this limestone. If so, it must have been barged down the River Witham. Lincolnshire Limestone was also utilised widely in both Cambridge and Oxford. The limestone is defined as 'porous shelly oolitic limestone, cross lamination often visible — defined by oyster rich layers, workable as a freestone, available in large blocks'.

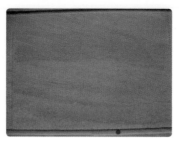

Exterior limestone cladding showing distinctive cross bedding. This is defined by the inclined sedimentary layers which truncate the beds beneath. The current direction in the original Jurassic shallow marine environment would have been from left to right.

Exterior limestone cladding showing clear graded bedding. This is defined by the sedimentary layers which show an upwards vertical grading of the sedimentary grains from coarse to fine.

On approaching the building, the limestone cladding can be examined. It displays well-developed cross bedding and graded bedding (see photos), similar to that seen in the Silver St pavements slabs (section 13, see text box for description). These bedding patterns are picked out by the sedimentary particles in the cladding slabs, which are mainly ooliths and broken shell fragments. This bedding reflects the original deposition in a shallow marine, warm water setting. The cross bedding indicates deposition by strong currents, while the graded sediments reflect periodic influxes of sediment into relatively calmer water than that indicated by the cross bedding.

To the north of the building, and separating it from the Cotswold Leisure Centre, is a high quality dry stone wall. This was also built from Clipsham Stone, by a team of stonemasons brought specifically to the site from Bath. The main entrance to the building, on the Tetbury Road side, is flanked by a dramatic area of South African Bushveldt black gabbro cladding. The same gabbro, but in its polished form, has been used effectively in the entrance foyer of the building as a fire surround. The foyer area inside the building is floored with beautiful polished Jura Limestone, of Upper Jurassic age, imported from southern Germany. This limestone contains many well preserved fossils, most notably, ammonites and belemnites (see photos). (Permission from St James Place is required for internal access to the building).

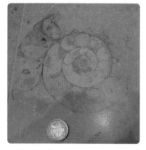

Ammonite cross section in interior hallway limestone floor.

Belemnite cross section in interior hallway limestone floor.

Directions: Proceed southwards along Old Tetbury Road and enter Castle Street.

On the corner of Castle Street and Silver Street stands the attractive Venetian (Palladian) style Cotswold Stone building now housing Lloyds Bank (built in 1790 as Pitt, Bowley and Croome's Bank). This architectural style was invented by Palladio in northern Italy, and was popular in the 18th Century in England. The Lloyds Bank building displays Venetian windows and both Ionic and Corinthian columns. It is the only Palladian style house in Cirencester. The stone used in its construction is high quality ashlar oolite, allowing a high standard of carving artistry to be achieved by the masons.

Lloyds Bank, Castle Street, a surprising example of a Palladian (northern Italy) style building, in oolitic limestone ashlar freestone. Note the 'Venetian' windows and both Ionic and Corinthian columns.

Many of the buildings in Castle Street are roofed with traditional Welsh slates, rather than Cotswold slates, as can be clearly seen from the south side of the street, looking to the buildings opposite. Welsh slates are typically thin and grey, being true slates, that were formed by the action of high temperatures and pressure on original shales and clays.

On the right (south) side of the street, just beyond W. H. Smith, is a men's clothing shop (R. Scott) which displays cladding of black gabbro with an igneous texture picked out by criss-crossing feldspar crystals. This gabbro originated from Rustenberg, South Africa, a huge igneous complex which is the source of most of the world's platinum. Polished black gabbro, distinguished by its small, predominantly dark coloured crystals, is a very popular cladding material, and there are other examples of its use in Cricklade Street, Dyer Street and St James Place.

Slates: slate is a good example of a metamorphic rock, created when fine grained sediments (clays, mudstones or volcanic ash) were subjected to directed pressure and increased temperature when buried quite deeply in the ground. The changes involved in metamorphism are more extreme than those involved in diagenesis and are related to burial (overburden load, with associated circulating waters): metamorphism involves recrystallisation and the associated formation of new minerals under the new pressure and temperature, with associated rock fabric changes. In slates the original bedding is folded due to tectonic compression caused by earth movements, and a new cleavage (surfaces along which the rock will split) develops parallel to the axial planes of the folds. The fissility of slates, causing the rock to break into flat, even surfaced slabs, is what makes them valuable for roofing. Unfortunately the slate miners commonly developed silicosis, a disease of the lungs caused by the inhalation of silica dust particles.

Directions: Continue eastward along Castle Street; on reaching the traffic lights turn right into Cricklade Street.

Grey granite pilaster in Cricklade Street,

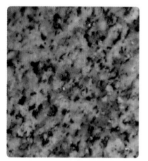

Granite pilaster close up showing prominent white feldspar and quartz crystals.

Detail of pink granite pilaster, showing abundant pink feldspar, quartz and mica crystals.

Fifty metres down the street on the left hand side, Costa Coffee has replaced a former Curry's shop, with complete restyling, but has retained the pilasters at both sides which are clad with a spectacular polished grey granitic igneous rock. This is crammed with laths of feldspar with a flow pattern, formed as they crystallised, from a molten, flowing magma. This process took place beneath ground ('intrusive' igneous rocks), where slow cooling allowed large crystals to form, not at the surface as a lava flow. Lavas, which cooled quickly at the surface ('extrusive' igneous rocks) are, in contrast, typified by much smaller crystals. The source of the granite used in this building is not known, but it is found very commonly in bank buildings throughout England that were constructed in the mid-20th century.

About 100 metres further down the same side of Cricklade Street, a very different type of granite can be seen. No 67 (at present occupied by Cotswold Curtains), opposite the junction with Ashcroft Road, displays red granite pilasters, footed by larvikite. This type of red granite was commonly used in late-19th to mid-20th century buildings, and was sourced from Peterhead, Scotland, though there are other similar granites utilised for building cladding. This distinctive red granite has an allotriomorphic granular texture (where none of the minerals in the rock shows any crystal faces), whereas the granite at Costa Coffee is idiomorphic (i.e. the minerals have good crystal shape). The principal component minerals in the red granite, red feldspar and white quartz, are of about the same dimensions, though biotite mica specks which glisten in the sunlight are much smaller than in the grey granite of the Costa Coffee building.

Pink granite pilaster in Cricklade St.

Directions: Turn northwards and take the first turn right along a narrow alleyway near Burtons clothes shop, turn right at the end, and it will bring you out at the Forum car park in front of the Police Station on the left hand side. The area from here eastwards was the Roman Forum. On the southwest corner, can be seen a remnant of a Roman pillar in front of Hooper's Court building.

This Roman pillar fragment has been preserved from the Roman Forum, which was the main open space of the Roman town of Corinium. Very few traces of the Roman town remain on the surface in Cirencester, though a number of houses have Roman remains in their basements. Note that the Romans seem to have preferred a gritty ragstone for outdoor construction, as in this pillar fragment, in preference to the more handsome oolite, presumably because the ragstone was stronger.

Limestone blocks utilised for entrance surrounds, showing well-developed cross bedding, picked out by layers of fossil shell fragments and ooliths.

The base of a Roman pillar in coarse ragstone, and even coarser ragstone for the pedestal. Note the modern addition of flint pebbles, originally formed as concretions in Cretaceous chalk, but later rounded by wave action on the sea shore.

Notice the water-worn cobbles set in the pavement around the pillar. These are of flint and probably originated from river gravels or beach shingle deposits in Chalk country, such as Wiltshire or Dorset.

Behind the Roman pillar is Hooper's Court, an apartment building that was constructed in 2006. The entrance and its surrounds have been made of ashlar stone and the dressings (footings and corners) are of an attractive brown limestone, contrasting with the now whitish limestone of the main stonework. Both these stones are of Athelstan Oolite (part of the Great Oolite of Late Bathonian age) and originated from Veizeys Quarry, near Tetbury. As can be seen in the photos, these limestones display prominent cross bedding and are rich in fossil shells, particularly gastropods and bivalves. The ooliths that make up the rock are clearly seen, along with the other features in the clean-cut faces of the stone dressings.

Building facing stone showing layers of shells (including a well preserved gastropod) and stylolites (calcite veins).

Directions: Walk along the pavement south-eastwards and turn right. This junction represents the crossroads of two former major roman roads, the north-west – south-east Ermin Street (today known here as Tower Street) and the north- east – south-west Fosse Way (today known here as Lewis Lane). Turn left at the traffic lights, along Watermoor Road. You will pass another small Roman Pillar on the right. Watermoor Church will be found further down on the right-hand side of the road.

Watermoor Church was built between 1847 and 1851. The architect was Sir George Gilbert Scott, who is known to have either designed or restored 26 cathedrals and 486 churches. Watermoor Church served the population of the southern part of Cirencester, which was the industrial area of the town. In terms of its building stones, the church is distinctive, and apparently unique for Cirencester, in being constructed primarily of a fine-grained brown sandstone in roughly shaped blocks, interspersed with occasional blocks of a shelly oolite. The sandstone has irregular fissility, displays small-scale cross-bedding, and includes occasional clasts (i.e. fragments) of shale.

According to Verey (1979, 1982), Watermoor Church is constructed of Jurassic Forest Marble. The Forest Marble is a formation which occurs at the top of the Great Oolite Group of the Middle Jurassic, and its 'type area' is the Wychwood Forest in Oxfordshire, from where some of the stone used in the interior of the church has originated. In the Cirencester region, the Forest Marble is a very variable rock unit, comprising clays (for example, at Shorncote, three miles to the south), limestones and sandy limestones. The brown sandstone building stone used in Watermoor Church is believed to have been sourced from a quarry along the London Road, Cirencester.

Around the ecclesiastical 'south' doorway (actually situated on the west side of the church, opposite the main entrance), four to five different rock types are evident.

Watermoor Church, 'south' doorway: pillars of fine sandstone, oolite ashlar dressings and brown sandstone wall masonry.

Watermoor Church: Close-up of the west wall masonry showing brown claystone flaky inclusions within the sandstone.

The pillars are of a fine grey calcareous sandstone, the quoins are of oolitic limestone and the infill blocks are of reddish brown, fine grained sandstone. In addition, there are dressings of oolite ashlar, and the south doorway has columns of a greenish-grey, even textured sandstone, which has also been utilised in the 'west window'. On this northern wall, some of the sandstone blocks contain clasts (fragments) of reddish claystone (see photo, above), while other blocks are of oolite. This would suggest that the source of the stone may have included interbedded sandstone and oolite.

The same grey calcareous sandstone appears to have been used inside the church, with the exception of a number of small pilasters around the altar which are composed of Ashford Marble (of Lower Carboniferous age, and typically from Derbyshire and of the same type as has been used in St John's Church for the font plinth). The architectural usage here is the same as with Purbeck Marble pillars and pilasters in mediaeval gothic buildings, that is in order to obtain a light-dark contrast. Purbeck Marble is a Jurassic shelly limestone from Dorset.

Watermoor Church: Close-up of the 'western' (north) wall showing oolite ashlar window dressings and rougher brown sandstone masonry on the main wall, with inset blocks of oolite.

Watermoor Church font, carved from spectacular Ashford Limestone, packed with fossil crinoids (close up on left hand side)

The font (to the left of the main doorway, near to the pulpit), is a spectacular example of polished Derbyshire Ashford Marble, and fossil crinoids ('sea lilies') can be seen in abundance. The font was donated by Rev. J. Stephens of St. Asaph Cathedral, Denbighshire, in 1972.

There are further geological connections, in the form of the stained glass windows. The rose window in the north aisle, almost concealed by the organ, was donated by the Geological Society (of London), at the initiative of Professor S. S. Buckman of the Royal Agricultural College, Cirencester. Buckman was a professor of geology, at a time when the college had a geology department. The window was created in 1850 by M & A O'Connor of Bristol. The Mary Anning window at Lyme Regis was also donated by the Geological Society at around the same time. Two further small stained glass windows on the north side of the main church entrance were also donated by Professor Buckman (and created by M & A O'Connor), in memory of his children Conrad and Elizabeth, who both died in 1852.

Directions: On exiting the church, turn left (north-west). Return to the traffic lights and turn right into Lewis Lane: continue, past a further set of traffic lights, to the Beeches car park, completing the main trail route.

OUTER CIRENCESTER

O n the outskirts of the town there are several further buildings of interest.
Refer to the map on the inside front cover (figure 1).

The grassed over
Roman amphitheatre.

Obelisk (18th century) outside
the amphitheatre.

The amphitheatre lay a short distance outside the south west defences of the Roman town of Corinium Dobunnorum, and was built in the later part of the first century AD. The two curving mounds enclosed a central area for shows and entertainments.

The amphitheatre is now grassed over, but excavations have shown that planking and dry stone walls supported wooden seats for the spectators. From loose blocks and fragments that can be found at the site, its construction appears to be from Great Oolite oolitic limestone, which is likely to have been sourced in the vicinity (note spoil mounds on west side of amphitheatre indicating local quarrying).

At the south west corner of the amphitheatre site, close to the entrance, can be seen the obelisk. This is constructed of oolite, with no inscription. It dates from the 18th century, and is one of several follies erected at the time in nearby Cirencester Park by the Bathursts. In the park there is a companion Doric pillar, erected in 1714 as a memorial to Queen Anne, a statue of whom adorns its summit. Amongst the follies scattered through Cirencester Park are buildings such as Pope's Seat where the poet Alexander Pope regularly sat. The grounds are immense and include a series of radiating tree-lined avenues, the main one of which extends some distance, to Sapperton village.

This cottage, located near the roundabout at the A429/ A419 junction, displays the fossils of seven ammonites, built into the walls, above the windows. Dated 1880, the house once belonged to the Cirencester Royal Agricultural College. A possible reason for the presence of the ammonites is because the first inhabitant of the cottage was a geologist.

The ammonites appear to be of the same type (arietitids of the *Coroniceras* type) that is known to occur in the Lower Sinemurian in England (Lower Jurassic, Lias Group), as in the well-known limestone pavement in the Blue Lias Formation at Lyme Regis (Dorset). The ammonites are not local to Cirencester, the nearest possible area in which they are common being the Bristol area (around Keynsham).

'Ammonite Cottage', with arrows pointing to the sites of ammonites inset in the walls (below).

It has been speculated that the house was occupied by the famous geologist James Buckman, who lived in Cirencester between 1846 to 1863 and was on the staff of the Royal Agricultural College, which in those days had a geology department (headed by Professor Harker). However, as 'Ammonite Cottage' was built in 1880, the house was clearly occupied by someone else who had a

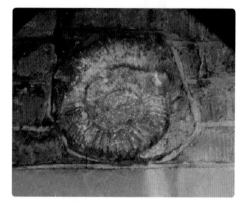

Ammonites inset into the walls of 'Ammonite Cottage'. At least two different species are represented.

liking for ammonites. James Buckman lived in a fine house in Dollar Street which is unfortunately no longer standing.

James Buckman was dismissed from the College (for espousing Darwinian ideas at the famous 1860 meeting of the British Association for the Advancement of Science, at Oxford), and he left Cirencester in late summer 1863, taking his three year old son, Sidney Savoury Buckman, with him to Dorset. S. S. Buckman became a very active researcher in Gloucestershire geology, but lived near Stroud and at Charlton Kings in his time in the county, never back in Cirencester (though he taught there for a while after Prof. Harker died) (Hugh Torrens, pers. comm. 2003).

The Royal Agricultural college: the main building in oolitic limestone with ragstone footings, a Victorian construction in the Tudor style.

The college was constructed in 1846, and comprises several Tudor style structures with a gothic (decorated) style chapel, the architects being S.W. Daukes and Hamilton.

The buildings are constructed of oolitic limestone from the Great Oolite, with cross-bedded shelly oolite footings (see photo below; note these are less weathered than freestone oolite nearby). Maybe it was this hard wearing quality which led to the cross bedded rock being used in footings for many 18th century buildings in Cirencester (e.g. those in Dollar Street). According to Richardson (1933), the building stone used for the construction of the college came from a quarry site just north of the college, which is indicated by a hollow in the landscape.

The two local resources used at the present time for building and construction in the Cirencester area are limestone (freestone, ragstone) and gravel for aggregate and manufacture of reconstituted Bradstone.

Limestone

Resources of Jurassic limestone across the Cotswolds are immense. Even allowing for the constraints imposed by fine quality freestone specifications, excessive overburden, environmental and socio-economic restrictions, reserves of quality freestone appear adequate for foreseeable future demand.

Several active large quarries in the region are located north of Cirencester, at Farmington (Northleach), Guiting Power and near Chipping Campden, in addition to numerous local quarries east of Cheltenham. A major use of Farmington Stone is for fireplaces, which have a good export market, in addition to building cladding and decorative building frontages. Daglingworth Quarry, just to the north of Cirencester, generates mainly crushed aggregates (chippings), used primarily for surfacing driveways and tracks. South of Cirencester, there are active limestone quarries at Veizeys Quarry, Tetbury, and Knockdown Quarry, near Malmesbury. Most of these modern quarries are working the Great Oolite limestones and supply stone for dry stone walling, building construction and roofing slates.

No underground mining is currently carried out locally for freestone (as it is in the Box and Corsham area of Wiltshire), although this has been active historically in parts of the region, such as around Cheltenham (see Price, 2007).

Gravel

Gravel is quarried extensively near Cirencester, in the area known as the Cotswold Water Park. The four Upper Thames gravel terraces have been extensively worked during the latter part of the 20th century, in quarries that form an arc extending eastwards from Somerford Keynes, south of Cirencester, as far as Fairford and Lechlade.

The gravels were derived by erosion from the limestone outcrops of the Cotswold escarpment by major river systems, developed in front of glaciers during the Pleistocene Ice Age. As a result, most of the gravel pebbles are composed of limestone, and are used for concrete and for reconstitution as the artificial Bradstone building stone.

The gravel excavations cannot be filled except with clean material because of the danger of contamination of water supplies, therefore the exhausted gravel pits are left to fill with water and are subsequently used for recreation purposes or as wildlife areas.

Opposite page: Farmington Quarry, working Great Oolite stone for ornamental use.